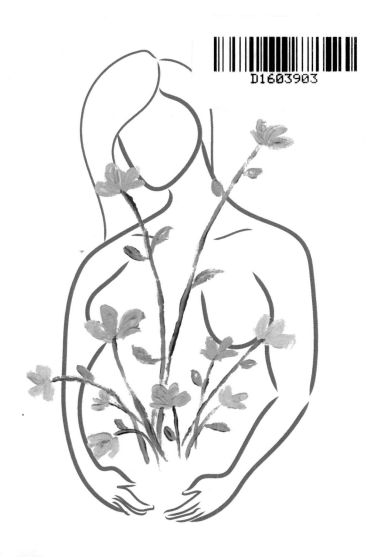

For when a child is born the mother also is born again."

—Gilbert Parker

ADVANCE PRAISE

If there is ever a time to learn to be present, it is during the very magical period of growing a new life inside of you. As someone who has experienced being very present and connected to myself and my first child while she was in my womb, and then the opposite with my second pregnancy, where I was feeling stressed and disconnected from my true self, I can attest that being in-tune with yourself and your unborn child makes a world of a difference in not only your overall experience of pregnancy, childbirth and postpartum, also I believe, it affects the temperament of the baby. The quality and the type of hormones and frequency of the thoughts/emotions the unborn child marinates in, while in utero, leaves a tremendous impact on both the mother and the child. Payal's honest, raw and authentic way of vulnerably sharing her personal story, coupled with a captivating writing style drew me into the book from the very first sentence, and had me wishing for more with each page I read. If I could wave a magic wand and make this book mandatory reading for all women who are preparing themselves for motherhood, I'd do it in a heartbeat. I believe that if all expectant mothers were tuned-in to themselves and this new, precious life growing within them, within one generation, the World would be transformed. That level of awareness and mindfulness would undeniably produce a rise in human consciousness. Thank you, Payal for pouring your heart and soul into this book baby. I'm holding the vision that it reaches all those women who are ready to have a truly magical pregnancy through presence.

Leyla Naghizada, Mama of two, Co-founder of Luxy Hair and Being Luca

ISBN: 979-8-9860164-0-5 (Paperback)

Front cover image by Cacau Mangabeira
Book design by espinosajavier.com
Illustrations by Sarah Boon

PAYAL KHURANA

PREGNANCY
and
PRESENCE

A Guide for
Surrendering
to the Moment
and Our Highest
Guidance
Within.

To you dear mothers,
For your courage, love and strength to bring souls into the
world.

To my spiritual guides.
Thank you for continuing to lead me from darkness into the
light.

To the divine feminine, my mother and my mother-in-law.
Thank you all for holding me, loving me and sharing your
endless wisdom.

EXTRA SUPPORT FOR YOU

Download 5 guided meditations just for you.

Visit http://www.payalkhurana.com/book/meditations
Follow the instructions on the page
Your download code is PPSMP321

CONTENTS

◇◇◇◇

– INTRODUCTION

It was a cold June morning in San Francisco; the yoga classroom was filled with women with their arms wrapped around their wombs warming their precious, unborn babies. My dear friend and I felt giddy to be taking our very first prenatal yoga class together. We stretched, we pulled and we sank into a child's pose just like other classes we had taken before; but this time the focus wasn't placed on just our own limbs. The instructor encouraged us to also become aware of the little unborn souls within our bodies. As the class was wrapping up, the teacher guided us to check in deeply to the emotions within us at the moment. Of the 18 women in the room, 16 of them were in the final trimester of their pregnancies. We shared our feelings openly and I heard a shared thread woven in all of our sharings.

"I'm going to be patient with this pregnancy because the first time I was pregnant I didn't slow down."

"I want to really soak up these last days before the baby comes, last time I was so focused on just the delivery of my baby."

"I'm relishing these last days with my first born, before everything changes again."

I sensed their sadness and disappointment, as well as their vulnerability. Many of these women admitted willingly how they were not really present during their first pregnancies. We were all there because we wanted something different than the journey of being distracted.

Most of these women, and possibly most women in general, rush through their first pregnancies. As a mindfulness facilitator for years, this doesn't surprise me. Most days we're all rushing through life chasing a future that doesn't exist yet. Most of our days are spent on auto-pilot. We aim to get all of our to-do's completed while there's a constant thoughtstream of distractions. We aren't paying attention to the actual moments we are in, so we're not present for our very own lives.

As soon as my pregnancy was celebrated, I was bombarded with advice, shoulds, all of the to-do's, so many medical appointments, and on top of all that came the obvious physical shifts within my body. It was dizzying. There I was, with a lot of absent doing and yet this pregnancy was one I craved for years. My mind tricked me into believing life was so much easier before when I wasn't pregnant and life would get better in the future when this pregnancy was done. The elusive moment that I'll be okay one day seems to never be here. It's a game that my mind plays that keeps me from soaking up each growing moment with my unborn. I remind myself - this moment IS the best moment of our lives because it's the only moment I can fully experience.

As I heard these women speak that day, I wondered quietly.

"Is it possible for me to choose to be more present during my first pregnancy?"

"Do I actually want to remember what it is to feel my baby within my womb or do I want to be distracted by all that I have to get done before they arrive?"

"Will I need to experience a second pregnancy too to be present with my baby and my body?"

"Why do I pretend that this life is just a dress rehearsal for the real thing that's yet to come?"

Can I choose to feel connected and be present during the process?

I felt a strong sense of purpose and desire to feel connected to my pregnant self and my baby throughout the joyful ride, not just at the celebrations of birth.

Presence isn't a place or a one time thing. It's a practice.

During the beginning of my pregnancy the layers of practice began to be revealed to me. There was the struggle of me wanting to escape the pain and discomfort just to "feel better" quickly. I pushed those feelings away while shoveling Pizza Hut pizza in my mouth in hopes it would numb the pain. If I wasn't distracting myself with things I needed to get done, I was busy scrolling away on Instagram and Facebook comparing my painful experience to the ease of some unknown woman online. I heard a constant voice in my head whispering I would never be as good as one of them. The mounting pressure overwhelmed me and I never thought I'd break free. And then there were moments when I leaned into my practice. I practiced leaning inward instead of running away. I learned to allow what was happening for me and accept it without resisting it. I was experiencing anger, fear, joy and sadness as they were instead of pushing them away only to experience them later.

I was grateful to already have a mindfulness practice and it was still challenging for me to not want to hide from what was happening. I continued to go back and forth, getting caught up in my mind's chatter and society's idea of what my pregnancy and motherhood should look like while also turning back to my practice. This book is my call to share stories from my personal journey. I'm sharing with you the practices that made the most impactful differences in helping me ground myself and trust my highest guidance within. As it can be said, God doesn't call the qualified, He qualifies the called. I feel called to share this work that will support mamas on their own wild ride of pregnancy and motherhood.

My wish for you is that you get to dive into the ocean of presence and surrender. My wish is for you dear reader to be able to check into the moments you are in now and uncover your own feelings and expectations and allow for more inner peace. I also wish that we learn to trust the pregnancy journey, releasing any resistance that blocks us from connecting to ourselves and to our own highest guidance within.

This book can and will guide you to more sincere and personal connection, if you are willing.

A couple notes:

"God" is used throughout this book. This may not resonate with you, bringing up thoughts or feelings you have of the idea of God. You can replace the word with the energy you connect to most which may be: the Higher Power, the Universe, Krishna, Allah, Buddha, Love, Source, your highest guidance within. I encourage you to not let language limit this Supreme Being. The name itself isn't of high importance for this practice, more so an acknowledgment of this Supreme energy existing for us to surrender to.

Gender pronoun shifts:

When I wrote this book I didn't know the sex of my baby, so throughout the book you might notice that I shift from her to him and he to she interchangeably.

— HAVE YOU *checked* IN WITH YOU?

P unch, punch, punch.

I was 10 weeks pregnant and punching away at the mits on my boxing coach's hands. I missed punch after punch. I knew something was off, he knew something was off, but we kept going.

The celebration of finding out I was pregnant was short lived. Tears of joy were very quickly replaced with tears of "Holy moly, am I really carrying a human around?" I had begun boxing before I was pregnant to lose weight. I kept boxing when I found out I was pregnant because it supported me in moving my body and releasing any anger I might be holding in my day to day.

"Give me 20 more punches," my coach said.
I grimaced.

"Ok, give me 40 more."
I sighed.
"Ok, make it 60."

My coach never let me waste even a moment. He took no excuses from me. So I took a deep breath and punched 60 times, even though my attention was focused on this huge responsibility of growing a new person. Boxing is one of those sports where you can tell exactly when the boxer's mind is anywhere other than on her form. I finished my 60 punches and my coach asked, "Yo, what's going on with you today?"

"I just... I have a lot on my mind," I whined. I was scared to even acknowledge what I was thinking about out loud.

My coach pressed on, "Do you want to talk about it?" I shared with him that I was overwhelmed with worries that something horrible could happen to my baby while she was in my womb. There, I said it.

Now that my husband and I had shared our joint initial excitement over those 2 delicate pink lines that appeared on a plastic stick, I felt the visceral weight of the responsibility of carrying this baby around. The intense desire to keep this baby safe and nurture her with every cell, fiber, inch of my being. I craved to make sure every part of him would be perfect and complete. I craved knowing how the future would turn out for him and whether we could live happily ever after. I wanted him safe in this nest, *always.* I was in control, yet so much not in control. I controlled the food I ate, I controlled the exercising I did, I controlled the number of stressful situations I allowed myself to be in. I did not control how his body would develop inside of me. I did not control how many fingers and toes he would end up with. I did not control if he had one health issue or another. I did not control the external of what unfolded in life. I was in control of my part of being and doing and the rest, that was up to God. It scared me more than anything my 35-year-old-self had ever feared before. I always thought I had control over my life, but now, there was a new piece of my heart that I would not have control over. Welcome to motherhood, Payal.

"Knock that off, you *choose* where you put your focus," Coach reminded me. He reminded me that yes, I could worry and have fearful thoughts, but it was up to me where I wanted to put my attention. As a mindfulness facilitator, I teach tools on becoming more aware of our attention. I coach people on how to choose which thoughts to put their attention on. Here I was boxing and my coach reminded me of the tool of choice in my attention. Coach walked out of the room and I was alone to finish up my session. Catching my breath, I closed my eyes just for a second, and took a deep breath. Where did I want to put my focus? I asked God for guidance. Within another breath, a line from a popular boy band song I hadn't heard in over 10 years popped into my mind.

Remembering the life giving words from that song, my heart swelled. I knew it was okay to let worry go. I acknowledged, yes, I had fear and I also had trust. I shifted my attention to trusting that God was spending time on my baby and that my baby was taken care of. What I had control over was where I put my attention, *energy flows where attention goes.*

As soon as we saw those precious two pink lines on that stick, I jumped into doing mode. I called my parents, called my in-laws, made an appointment for my first sonogram, and googled my heart out on all things pregnancy. I downloaded apps to keep me informed of what was happening with me and my baby; I kept searching for someone else to educate me on what I should be doing in these precious weeks. What I mostly found were warning signs, be on high alert mama! (Like we aren't already on high alert as the hormones surge through our bodies or something). The to do's were all done--yet did I ever take a moment to pause and ask myself what I was feeling in the moment? It was easy to get so caught up in the doing and analyzing that I forgot about being, even as a mindfulness facilitator. I needed to *intentionally* give myself space to check in with my being way beyond any of the doing. And sometimes I did so much that my body fell into exhaustion and then I was forced into sitting still where all I could do was face myself and my emotions I kept running from.

This time it was boxing that got me to see that I had been running so much that my being needed my attention. I always imagined that I would be elated to be pregnant, but I never knew being pregnant came with feelings of doubt, concern and worry. After my boxing session, I got into my car and snapped out my phone. I pulled up YouTube and typed in "God Must Have Spent A Little More Time on You" and I watched the video of what I thought must have been a song about romance. As I listened, I felt every fiber of me shiver with presence as I watched a video about a mother's love for her son. In that moment I experienced insight that transformed me. In times of overwhelm and stress, if I was willing to take a moment to check in with myself and my emotions, I would be able to receive what I truly need.

"Presence is the practice of checking IN instead of checking out."

Your turn
– LET'S CREATE SPACE AND CHECK IN WITH YOU.

For this time, I'd like for you to put the side to do lists. This time and space is *for you* to allow yourself to feel, sense and be with no one else but yourself..

Before answering the questions below, try this on: Close your eyes. Place your hands anywhere you feel close to your baby: on your stomach, on your heart, wrapped together, anywhere that feels most comfortable. Imagine yourself getting close to your baby as they grow. Imagine that every cell in your body and their body has its own set of lungs. Take a deep breath in with every single cell and a deep breath out. Do this practice repeatedly until you feel ready to open your eyes.

What are you feeling right at this moment?

Take another deep breath and answer the following question by freeflow writing (writing whatever comes to your mind even if it doesn't make sense or it doesn't feel possible).

As you read the words on this page, how does it feel in your body at this exact moment? If your answer is, "I don't know." Feel it. Allow your awareness to fully come into your entire body. And in this moment, remind yourself to allow it to be exactly as it is. Whether it's pleasant or not pleasant. Let it be.

Where is your body positioned now? What does it feel like to be in the position you are in?

How is it in the heart at this moment? Allow what you feel in your heart to be as it is. Not right, not wrong. Just as it is.

Ask your heart: What do I need right now for me? And listen in deeply to what comes through.

"When you lose touch with inner stillness, you lose touch with yourself. When you lose touch with yourself, you lose yourself in the world."

-Eckhart Tolle

— WHERE
is your
WORTH?

W hen I was young I imagined that when people were born into this world there was a gold star of worthiness planted into their being. This gold star told the world that they deserved all good things, to be surrounded by other shiny people and to live a full shiny, beautiful life. Each step they took told the world just how "meant to be here" they were. Their fullness oozed onto the sidewalks. They had no need to want anything because even when they did, it easily slid their way. They didn't have to work hard for anything because their shininess made things happen so effortlessly. Their lives unfolded just like the fairy tales said they would, happily ever after. The shiny ones were meant to be seen, surrounded and admired for their beauty and ease.

I, on the other hand, must have somehow been skipped when God was planting that gold star of worth. For me, I had to get up at 5 am, blow dry my natural waves to stick straight, slather on concealer to cover up those horrid dark under-eye circles, pop in the green color contacts covering up any speck of brown in my eyes and squeeze into the latest fashion trends to tell the world, "Look, I'm shiny too! Please, please accept me!" Anytime

I got what I wanted in life, I would wonder - "When will this get taken away?" or "This won't last anyhow." When I did get attention, I thought I should keep myself small because -- who was I to take up space. Somebody should definitely shove me back in a corner because that is where I deserved to be. This shine aka worth was given to all the others and I tripped all over myself hoping that one day I would also get to be just as shiny.

I chose to look to the external for validation that I was inherently enough as I was. I looked to the friend who had it all -- confidence, looks, creativity-- and I attached myself to them because if I was their friend, then I was worthy. Anytime that shiny person chose me as a friend, I showered them with gifts and love just so they wouldn't find out how unworthy I was of their presence. I looked to the highly respected college degree because if I had that degree then I was worthy. I looked to the man who had already been bestowed a golden star to date me because if I had his attention then I must be worthy. Before I got pregnant, I looked to the work that I did because if I had the career everyone wanted then I would be worthy. If only I had the things, the people, the job - then and only then would I be allowed to have a space in this world.

Let's fast forward to my mid 30s, externally I had lined things up to tell the world that yes I was enough - I was doing work that I felt fulfilled by, I was married to the love of my life, and I was growing a miracle inside of me. Early on in my pregnancy, I was very nauseated to the point where my bed became my home for hours during the day. I needed to be as close as possible to the bathroom, so I settled in. This made it very challenging to get any work done. I needed to move at a slow pace to not upset my stomach. My usual quick movements slowed down many levels and demanded more of my attention and purpose. Each movement had to be intentional, there was no room to multitask only enough space to get the essentials done. What used to be a simple 2 flights of stairs became, "UGH 2 whole flights of stairs!" This was maddening. Even breathing moved slower, which all meant I had less output with work. My energy level and nausea were things that I had no control over and parts of me kept fighting that I even felt this way. I noticed, as each day passed, the less work I was doing, the more frustration, guilt and shame I started to feel. I kept pushing up against the reality of how my body was feeling and the feeling of depression started to seep in as fewer and fewer things got done around me.

"I really should be answering those emails."

"Get UP and go into the office!"

"Why does it even have to feel this way?" Other people don't get this nauseous.

"It really shouldn't be that hard to function right now."

"Did we get pregnant too quickly? I should be focused on my career!"

"What's the point of all of this anyway?"

The voice would speak and my body would deflate. Without doing anything I already felt like a failure. The heavy voice of "Get up!" would come and a strong force would push me to get up to continue to earn my worth. My heart would hear those words and my body would sink with nausea that had nothing to do with already being pregnant. With all this physical work it felt easier to just give up on doing anything beyond existing.

One evening, two friends invited me over for dinner. They asked which foods were currently making me nauseated and without warning tears trickled down my cheeks. It surprised me and my friends. I shared how I hadn't expected to be this nauseated. I hadn't expected to be this useless in my day to day. How could I appear shiny if I wasn't actually producing anything? How could I continue to portray that I was enough, moving as slow as molasses? When I was growing up the people around me didn't ever have an opportunity to stop and rest. I began to understand that the culture we live in doesn't value rest and not producing anything. If I wasn't being productive, what value did I have to this world? If I didn't have my work that fulfilled me, then what could I look to tell me that I was actually enough?

One of my friends quickly reminded me that I was not useless. My body was currently a vessel of creation of another human being. How was just that fact not of value? If one day our baby's brain was being built, wasn't that being productive? So even if I was doing this valuable thing, why did I not feel worthy? Why did I continue to beat myself up and silently remind myself that I missed out on that gold star of worth? When my friend shared this with me, I realized I was in a different kind of productivity. Not the type I was used to, which pushed me to look at my relationship with the work I do and the story I associated it with. I discovered I relied on the work to fill me up, to give me the belief that I was worthy.

Pregnancy gave me the opportunity to look deeper at how I related to my worth. At my core beyond the external, did I actually believe I was not just as worthy as every other gold star recipient? Couldn't I be worthy regardless of what my outside looked like and what I was doing on a day to day? I allowed myself to spend time with that question, leading me to look at my core beliefs of my worth of being on this planet and what I wanted to shift. First and foremost, I began to recognize that I no longer believed that only some people got this gold star of worth. I reminded myself that the very fact that I am given this sacred opportunity to be alive and experience human life entails that yes I AM worthy.

Every single one of us is meant to BE here no matter what we choose to do, including me.

No person, no thing, no job could make us more worthy than we already are. We are already enough. In Rumi's words, " You are the universe in ecstatic motion."

I begin to work with this concept:

Be, Do, Have.

This concept means to first look into our way of *being*. The way of our being influences the things we choose to *do*, which leads us to *have* what is aligned with our current way of being and the things we desire. For example, looking at who I believe myself to be first: If I believe I am worthy, I won't look to others or my appearance or material things to give me my worth. I will act with love and acceptance towards myself and then whatever I choose to do with my time - pregnant or not - will be inspired by that connection. I allow myself space to be as I need to be without the worry about who is by my side or the type of work that I do or how others view me. If I connect to my innate worth, I honor myself patiently in my journey wherever I am at. I'd allow myself

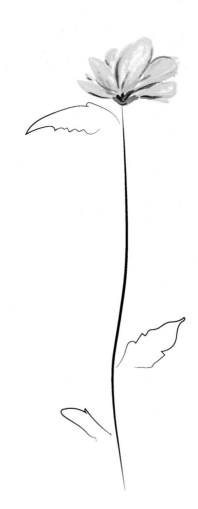

"*You are loved just for being who you are, just for existing. You don't have to do anything to earn it.*"

-Ram Dass

to lie in bed for as long as I needed when I needed. If I felt in my being my innate worth, it wouldn't matter at all how much I produced on a day to day. It's being, doing, then having. We live in a world that tells us in order to be, we must have. It's up to us to focus on our being first.

Let's Practice Being

Read over the practice below and do your best to practice by memory with your eyes closed.

Take a deep breath. Take one more deep breath, noticing how your stomach expands as you inhale and contracts as you exhale. Allow yourself to connect more to presence as you take 2 more deep breaths. With your eyes closed, find a place within yourself you could consider your center. Maybe your heart, maybe the place between your eyebrows, maybe your solar plexus. Find the center that directs you inward. Sit with yourself in this place, breathe as you fill in the blank:

I am

. . . .

. . . .

. . . .

. . . .

. . . .

. . . .

. . . .

. . . .

. . . .

A preacher named Joel Osteen says that the words that come after "I am" are an invitation to our lives. So if we say "I am tired," we're inviting even more tiredness. If we say "I am joyful," we invite in more joy.

Take 3 more breaths and invite the way of being you would like more of in your life.

I AM

— BEND LIKE *Bamboo*

Why do we worry? Where does stress come from?

This morning I caught my mind spinning into worry about a future work event. I watched silently as I created the story that it would be a complete disaster.

No one is going to even show up.

Watch me fall over with my big, pregnant belly and heels.

I won't even be able to find a dress that fits. I'll never be able to get anything done with all of this nausea.

Then I took a very deep breath. I asked the source that lives deep inside me to help. I asked God to give me insight on how to deal with my worry. I asked spirit to tell me how I can trust that all is happening as it should.

God's answer?

For me to look around—at the moment I was in. To notice the love, the beauty that surrounds me in the now. That moment, that event that I worry about will ALSO be filled with love, if I let it. The worries that I'm allowing in my mind can all be addressed in the moment when it arrives *if they actually manifest.*

The thing that we do with our worries is we block out the good. How can we imagine the wonderful part of life, if we're busy thinking of how things MIGHT go wrong? How can we ever predict how amazing something just might turn out to be?

Ancient Japanese teachings encourage us to be like bamboo. Bamboo is strong and sturdy, yet it bends and doesn't break in the wind. It becomes fluid, it harmoniously flows with not one battle against the wind.

Worries are like choosing to fight against the wind. So today, let's choose to step away from worry. Let's choose to surrender into the moment and to bend with the wind whenever we need to.

— WHAT ARE *you* EXPECTING?

In my mind:

I am beautifully pregnant with my baby. I look, smell, and feel like a glowing goddess. Each morning I wake up grateful for my growing bump. My husband slowly pulls me closer as he wakes up, whispers in my ear how beautiful I am, and whisks me into the kitchen to make me my favorite breakfast. And, oh, also gives me all of his undivided attention for all moments of the day. Nothing is more important than me. Everyone happily supports all of my choices. People I don't know stop me to tell me how I'm glowing and how lucky this baby must be. People hold doors open for me as I walk on air floating through life with my newfound pregnant happiness.

In my reality:

I am uncomfortably pregnant with my baby in my ever growing womb. My bump, my belly, my arms, my legs, my double chin- everything is BIG. I wake up in the morning to look over and find the bed empty, my husband already gone to work. I'm fighting for his attention with the growing responsibilities of becoming the sole provider for some time to come. Sometimes even the phone gets more attention than I do. People voice their disagreements with my choices, didn't I know that they knew best? They make sure I know their opinions and judgments of my choices. People I don't know ask me if I'm having a boy or a girl or *twins!* While I'm out minding my own business running errands, I get asked when the baby is finally coming and while impatiently waiting for an answer, they graciously share their horror stories of birth.

I've always heard it's important NOT to have expectations--yet who doesn't have expectations? Who doesn't already picture how they would like an event to go? Or how they would like someone to treat them? Or how a certain relationship "should" be? Most of us flippantly give advice not to have expectations. Though we can certainly spend time analyzing whether we have expectations or not.

◇◇◇

It's even more important for a person to notice if they have an emotional attachment to the expectation.

◇◇◇

Are our feelings about the expectation blocking us from peace or allowing what actually is?

For example, during my pregnancy, I had an expectation for my husband to always be sweet and kind to me because I was carrying our child. That was the expectation. I was emotionally attached to the expectation because the times he acted differently than what my mind wanted, I became triggered and felt like it was a personal attack rather than something that had to do with him. I wanted, I needed him to be the way I saw him in my mind. Loving, romantic and kind. There was no room for him to have a tough day. No room for him to be angry or impatient. No room for him, just room for me and my mind. I didn't have control over him so it made me feel even more out of control overall.

A mentor of mine gave me an exercise so I could zoom out on my expectations. It encouraged me to look at the expectations I had of others, what was I wanting from that expectation or what would I receive if that expectation occurred. Then I would take a pause to reflect on how I would feel if I would remove my attachment to this expectation occurring. Next, mirror the expectation(s) back to myself and see how I felt. Looking at how I felt, allowed for an opportunity to discover what I needed from me, not anyone else. After the exercise I could ask myself if I wanted to keep the expectation I had of the other person or choose to let it go.

For example:

Expectation: My husband must always be nice and loving during my pregnancy. Always.

What would I receive if that occurred: I would receive the feeling of comfort, the feeling of being supported and the feeling of being accepted.

How would I feel if I were to free myself of this attachment to needing his behavior of constant kindness? I would feel more empowered and self confident. I would feel more trusting. I would have less of my focus on the picture in my mind and I would receive him as he is.

I would then say the expectation back to myself. Payal, I expect you to always be kind and loving. When I said it out loud,

I noticed I experienced a caged, controlled feeling. I felt like there was no room for me to be authentic.

When I experienced that sensation, I realized what I was really looking for was compassion for me from me.

Your turn.

Let's practice looking at our expectations

Before beginning the writing exercises, take a pause by focusing in on 5 deep breaths.

Bring to mind one expectation you have of someone close to you.

Expectation:

. . . .

. . . .

. . . .

. . . .

. . . .

. . . .

. . . .

What would you receive if that expectation occurred?

. . . .

. . . .

How would you feel if you were to free yourself of your attachment to your expectation?

Say the expectation to yourself out loud.

. . . .
. . . .
. . . .
. . . .
. . . .

What do you notice as you say your expectation to yourself?

. . . .
. . . .
. . . .
. . . .
. . . .
. . . .
. . . .
. . . .

Are you willing to let that expectation go for just today?

. . . .
. . . .
. . . .
. . . .
. . . .
. . . .

Try the exercise again with another expectation you notice within yourself.

—WHY

Because this life we see is colored with our thousands of thoughts and perceptions of the past and what we think might happen in the future.

Because when we are mindful, when we are present to the actual moment we begin to see reality as it is.

Because even when I'm too busy, too tired, too everything, a simple 2 minutes of it creates even a little connection.

This morning as I sat in the tub after my morning practice, I was lost in my random thoughts when I looked at the soap bubbles on my hand. Without being distracted by anything else I saw how they sat so perfectly, how they seemed to clean and illuminate my hand. I could actually see when I decided to quit paying attention to the thoughts of things that weren't relevant to what was happening in front of me.

> Why meditate?
> Because this life is precious.
> It can be so easy to forget and take the simple things for granted.
> Because the ONLY guaranteed moment we have is the moment we are in - so why sleepwalk through it by just paying attention to our thoughts in our mind?

Why not meditate and learn how to train your attention?
Why not meditate and learn how to choose where you
give your power?
Why not meditate and learn what it means to actually see
reality without attachment?

I recall leading a meditation outside once with all beginners.
We sat in a circle in the middle of campus as students rushed
around us to get to class. The meditators shared how vulnerable
they felt--yet, when they opened their eyes after just 10 minutes
of being internal, one person shared excitedly, "I can actually
see the colors in the tree. Everything looks clearer now." It's like
having wiped your glasses clean after a day of walking around
with dirt on them.

So I ask yet again -

Why not meditate and learn to see beyond the millions of
perceptions, preferences, controlling attachments of your mind?

— WHAT *do you* HAVE?

To buy

> Top of the line stroller
> Organic Diapers
> Wipes
> Crib
> Breastpump

One morning as I sat in my writing chair with the weight of my belly stacked upon my backbone, a thought came to the surface wishing for this experience to hurry on up. Another thought followed, if only I had all of the physical things I needed *then* I could take a sigh of relief and I would instantly feel better. A part of me believed that once I had all things on my "to buy" list, I would be prepared as an A list student ready for the baby to arrive. Though it felt like the list kept growing, the girl that loved to cross things off of her lists felt a sense of freedom each time she would check one item off and the illusion of readiness came through. I created the idea that I was prepared for our baby to arrive armed with all of my much needed supplies. As a society we support this idea that if we just have all the best baby items we would be ready to take on arguably the greatest role in our lives. All a person has to do is google "new mom must haves" and copious blogs will appear telling you just what you need to be *the* number 1 mom. The "to have" list that most people can easily forget to cultivate are our inner needs: self compassion for when we make mistakes, surrender for those rollercoaster moments that are bound to happen, trust in our own wisdom and our body's wisdom, patience to move one moment at a time in this brand new phase of transition. This is the list that we as a majority gloss right over as we rush to get it all right before we welcome a new soul into our worlds. As I looked over my to buy list, to the side of it I wrote "To cultivate". This list would be my lifeline. It would be there for me as I navigate the last stretch of my pregnancy and prepare me the most for motherhood. This cultivation is a continuation, it's what we practice coming back to over and over.

To cultivate

> Self-Compassion
> Trust in my body
> Patience in the moment I am in now
> Surrender to God
> Gratitude

Cultivating this "must have" list of inner needs is something we can all take a moment to consider. In challenging times, what gets you through? What creates the feeling of "I will"? I will myself get up even if every bone in my body wants to lay here? In habitual doing, it's easy to forget what fills us up to manage the unknowns. It's in our habitual doing that we check out and move straight into autopilot forgetting what way of being we might need to tap into in our unexpected moments. Or even what quality of being do we want to be most connected to even when we are doing the same task over and over and over. For me, one quality I begin with is gratitude. In the tough moments of nausea and struggle with this growing body I challenged myself to ask the question: How can I express gratitude in this moment? In the not so tough moments, gratitude gives me the opportunity to recognize what is already here.

The quality of our lives is in the quality of our attention.

If we can notice what we're grateful for right now while it's actually happening, it's very unlikely that we will think back to believing it was better in the past or think forward in believing that the future holds the key to the end of our suffering.

Towards the end of my pregnancy I began a committed gratitude practice. I wanted to start cultivating the qualities that would support me in the most challenging times, not only in pregnancy but in motherhood as well. Every morning I would wake up and sit with my pen and paper and find ten things I was truly thankful for. One morning, I gave gratitude for noticing the ease of crawling into bed after a day of little sleep and lots of errands. It was the motion of getting under my blankets and allowing myself to rest that I felt so grateful for. Some mornings I sat and tapped my pen on the paper and waited for gratitude to show up because I didn't seem to be finding any but I made sure I was consistent. **Gratitude not only helps us check in the moment we are in, it also helps us zoom out and to see the**

bigger picture when the zoomed in picture seems like that's all there is. During the last weeks, I was very zoomed in and attached to my thoughts of, "Oh what was that movement? Is it THE time?!" "What aches NOW?" "Is labor ever going to come?" The practice of gratitude every morning allowed me to connect with myself before the baby came. It gave me the opportunity to acknowledge the friends who were helping along the way. Gratitude allowed me to zoom away from the things I might not have perceived as "good" and open my eyes to the infinite possibilities around me. The brain focuses on things that it perceives as harmful. Our brains just want us to survive, so it is up to us to step back and help our brains to notice more than just the things that may seem wrong.

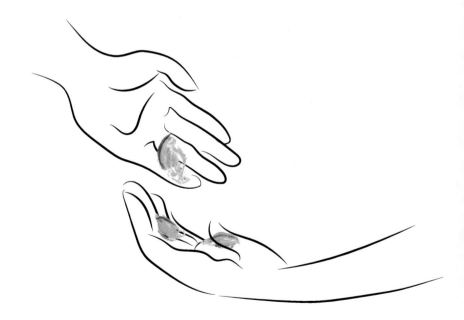

Let's Practice: What's on your cultivation list?

Before we begin to take a look at what we want to cultivate during pregnancy, let's begin our practice with centering ourselves into the moment. Take a few moments to read the section that follows and then find a comfortable space to sit and at least ten to fifteen minutes of uninterrupted solitude, close your eyes and practice.

Begin with long, slow deep breath. Take two if you feel the call. Gently concentrate on a few breaths, noticing the movement of air through your nose, down your throat and into your lungs. Bring your attention to your womb as you breathe, noticing as you inhale it expands and allowing it to collapse inward as you exhale. Breathe at a depth and pace that is most comfortable to you, there's no need to rush or no way to get this wrong. Allow yourself to sit with your breath, noticing when your attention wanders anywhere other than your breath. Do this for as long as you'd like and then open your eyes, grab a pen and answer the questions below.

Pick three qualities to describe the type of mother you'd like to be. What are they?

(1) _____

(2) _____

(3) _____

"*Where have you taken your sweet song?*
Come back and play me a tune.

I never really cared for the things of this world.
It was the glow of your presence
that filled it with beauty."

-Hafiz

What practices could support you to be closer to these qualities?

Being and doing go hand in hand. Brainstorm what you could do in this time before your child arrives to cultivate these qualities of being.

Look around where you are. What is something you can feel gratitude for in THIS moment? Take a moment to give gratitude by saying Thank you either silently or outloud.

After acknowledging your gratitude, how do you feel?

— WHERE DO
your thoughts
WANDER?

As I sat at 40 weeks and 2 days one morning, I opened up the book *As a Man Thinketh*. In the book James *Allen* explains that the body is directly affected by the thoughts we think.

"At the bidding of unlawful thoughts the body sinks rapidly into dis-ease; at the command of glad and beautiful thoughts it becomes clothed with youthfulness and beauty."

Reading that sentence felt so timely: as soon as I hit 40 weeks all my doubtful, fearful thoughts decided to make a space in my home.

"Is the baby still okay in there?"

"Will the baby be too big to exit my body if the baby keeps growing?"

"There is so much stretching, is it supposed to be this painful?!"

WHAT ARE YOU EXPECTING?

I ruminated on these thoughts for a few days, and my body responded. The aches felt bigger, my jaw locked at night and my awareness of the 1000 thoughts of doubt were louder. I gave myself space to pause and wonder, where had my doubt and worry thoughts been coming from? Thoughts can become a tidal wave if we don't direct them. One thought will rise up and another will follow; if we place our attention on those thoughts they grow bigger. If we choose to let the worry thoughts wash through us instead of crashing into them, they move on by. I was half heartedly directing myself to find a mantra. Mantra comes from the two words in Sanskrit "manas" meaning mind and trayate meaning "to free". A mantra frees our mind from anxiety and illusion. This mantra would support me to direct my thoughts to what I want rather than letting my worry and doubt thoughts swallow me up. It was easy for me to say I would do it later and later, only to not follow through. After I read James's words, I chose to sit and do a mantra meditation.

I repeated to myself that my body and spirit already knew what to do at birth. At first my body felt stiff, it didn't believe me but I continued. "My body and spirit already know what to do during birth." I felt a slight shift. Tension softened and energy began to rise. I had been attempting to understand the essence of surrender and I realized that listening and paying attention to the energy I had been creating was the way. Through trust, through this mantra, I could filter out the unnecessary voices in my head and let my body do what it was designed to do.

PAYING ATTENTION

Set a timer for 5 minutes. As thoughts enter your mind, write them down as a stream of consciousness. There's no need to interrupt, judge or challenge. This is a practice for us to pay attention to our attention. Begin by taking 3 breaths, allowing your attention to follow each part of your inhales and exhales. Riding on the waves of your breath and allowing yourself to be aware with no need to react just a space to pay attention

Looking at the thoughts you wrote down, do you notice how they might be influencing how you experience the moment?

*"Thoughts are neither as pure
nor as powerful as you are."*

- *Unknown*

Look back at what you wrote, which thoughts do you want to let wash through you?

. . . .
. . . .
. . . .
. . . .
. . . .
. . . .
. . . .
. . . .
. . . .
. . . .
. . . .
. . . .
. . . .
. . . .
. . . .
. . . .

Which thoughts would you like to be feeding your body?

. . . .
. . . .
. . . .
. . . .
. . . .
. . . .

What mantra could serve you as you move throughout your days?

— ARE YOU *willing to* QUIT COUNTING?

O ur society is obsessed with numbers.

We want to know how far along we are. We want to know where on the scale we measure up. We want to know how much we weigh and maybe even how much our neighbor weighs. We're always placing everyone up against the chart of "normal" based on numbers.

I was somewhere in the middle of my last trimester when I woke up one night, as usual to go to the bathroom, when my mind began to run.

Ugh, my body is so heavy. Can I actually get BIGGER?

There is just no way, no way, I can make it 6 - 8 MORE weeks.

Once the baby is out I will be so free, why can't this go faster?!

Thought after thought continued to create anxiety. I turned my focus to my breath. I chanted a mantra meditation. I even counted sheep. Nothing seemed to calm my thoughts; I kept coming back to analyzing where my pregnancy was going and how I would ever make it through the rest of the time. I believed that the baby would come out THEN I would be able to move around and be free. I was waiting until that moment and then I would be able to let go of all of this tension my body was holding. I was pushing my ability to experience peace and joy out to months *far ahead in time.*

It is a story my mind likes to weave - the future holds the key to my happiness, my release to just be free from any suffering. It's this part of my brain that always wants to race ahead to the "finish line" rather than live in the moment I'm in.

Can my baby just hurry up and get out of my womb?

Can't I just already be in the great part of my career, the part where I've "made it"?

Isn't it going to be much better over there than here?

Yet, at the same time I also tend to think of the past when we REALLY had it good. I was so free before, I never worried about anything back then. It was such a great time *then*, not now. It is always better in the past and in the future. But what about right now?

My last ditch effort to calm my thoughts was getting out my phone to find something to read. I dug into my email to look at some of the newsletters I rarely open. One was titled Quit Counting. It was a meditation newsletter by Nayaswami Devi. He shared how interesting it was that we are always creating restlessness in the moment we're in because we need to get to the next part. We push past the present just to get to one hour or to some later time in the day and then the rest of the time we expend energy just fixated at the end. There's this internal anxiety to rush beyond the moment because it's not good enough, not shiny enough, not joyful enough. It's the silent suffering that tells us we won't suffer later if we can just through this time. It will get better because as society would say, "The best is yet to come." As I lay there and read, I continued to realize that every week I was counting down just to get to the birth. My present moment had zero value, I just needed to get through it. That thought made me pause. Did I really want to create this type of experience for myself? Did I really want to whine and cause myself suffering each week by reminding myself and my husband just how LONG I still had left?

No, I didn't.

What I really wanted was to slow down. To stop criticizing and judging the journey. I wanted to stop anticipating the feeling that the only moment that mattered was the end. So I did.

I quit keeping track of exactly which week I was in. Yes, I knew how many weeks I was each time I went in for my doctor's visits but I was no longer having that number be my focus. I was no longer just reaching for that endpoint. I focused my awareness back to the moment I was currently living in. The only moment we can actually fully truly experience.

Let's Check in

How has your relationship with how far along you are been?

. . . .
. . . .
. . . .
. . . .
. . . .
. . . .
. . . .
. . . .
. . . .
. . . .
. . . .
. . . .
. . . .
. . . .

"You get to decide what to worship."

-David Foster Wallace

Are you counting? How does it make you feel to count?

Are you focused on the outcome or the present moment?

A simple way to bring us back to the present moment is to focus in on one of our senses. What do you hear right now in this moment? Close your eyes and tune in to all the sounds around you, let that be your meditation for at least 2 minutes.

— PATIENCE *and the* WAITING GAME

I always thought I knew what patience meant. I heard it all the time growing up, "Be patient"....The subtext was what you want is coming your way.

So that is what I've carried with me, patience is just the in-between space of wanting and getting.

Patience is the thing we do to calm the anxiety and the nerves of our egos that want it all. Right. This. Second.

Patience is the thing we turn to in order to psych ourselves up to keep reaching for that *dangling* carrot.

But as I grow, as I dive deeper into my practice of mindfulness, I'm learning that patience has nothing to do with calming my nerves in order to get what I want.

Patience is that reminder to be present to the moment we're in.

Patience is the gift of the in-betweens.

Patience is the reminder that there is no other place to be -physically or mentally - other than right here.

I've been lucky enough to help bring a bonsai tree back to life.

I've watched little brown leaves slowly turn into green leaves and then into even brighter green leaves.

I've watched the tree begin to breathe again.

I've watched myself getting excited about the whole tree being green - and then I remember, patience is the beauty of where it is right now. Not where I hope for it to be in the future.

In the great words of Henri Nouwen:

"Let's be patient and trust the treasure we look for is hidden in the ground on which we stand."

MEET MY *friend* THE ROSE BUSH

I've watched this rose bush go from being teeny tiny to now almost growing out of its original pot. I've watched as bright green rose buds start appearing and with each day they slowly unfold into bright pink roses.

They bloom for days and then their petals begin to slowly wither. Each withering petal falls to the ground, stripping the rose of life. Slowly what was a rose becomes a dead flower.

The most amazing part to watch is right next to the dead rose, a new baby vine full of life starts to grow — it creates a fresh new green arm to bloom a brand new rose.

The life cycle of the rose mirrors to me times that are difficult. The pain of resisting opening to bloom. The pain of thorns thrusting from the stem ready to pierce anyone that may attempt to pluck the rose from its comfort. The pain of a bud finally reaching full bloom only to begin to wither away into death.

As I'm moving through a transformation, I want to stay closed like the bud. I hold on tight to the old me that's comfortable. There's no need for me to bloom, I've been good here for quite some time…why do I need to unfold only to lead a part of myself to death?

Yet, transformation happens by stepping into the hard and the painful.

I've noticed through the stretching to be bigger, through the heartache, there is also that bright green vine quietly waiting to be born.

This new vine sits inside waiting for me to accept, waiting for me to quit running, waiting for me to stop wishing things were easy. And most importantly the vine sits waiting for me to be ready for a death and a new birth.

The rose bush waits for that moment so it can start growing a fresh new vine of life—that vine that is only born because of the difficult. That vine nudges me to grow and to learn what I'm capable of.

And maybe I want easy, but difficult is what makes us bloom.

Difficulty is what got me to live to being thirty three.

Difficulty is what got my parents to America to build a life for themselves.

Difficulty is what gets us all to create the amazing things we have today.

— PREPARE FOR
the DELIVERY

L et's shift from the external to the internal for this exercise. Before we begin, allow some softness into your space. I invite you to remove any masks of masculinity that tighten and force and say "Make it happen". Let's try on the vulnerability of trust of the unknown, hope and *surrender*.

Close your eyes and imagine yourself in the place you may give birth.

What do you see around you? Who is there with you?

. . . .

. . . .

. . . .

. . . .

. . . .

. . . .

. . . .

. . . .

How does it make you feel to be in that space?

Free write for 10 minutes how you *want* to feel the day you go into labor and while you are laboring. This space is one without judgment, free writing allows whatever wants to be expressed in you to arise. If you notice any tension, take a few deep breaths, dance around the room while holding your womb and begin again.

Look at what you wrote and choose 3 words that call your attention.

. . . .

. . . .

. . . .

. . . .

. . . .

Using those 3 words, create a short sentence you can weave into a mantra for yourself. Keep it short, simple, and meaningful.

. . . .

. . . .

. . . .

. . . .

. . . .

. . . .

. . . .

. . . .

Take a moment to consider if there's anything physical that can support you to feel the way you'd like. Maybe a bracelet to remind you of the feeling as you call your baby into this physical world. Maybe sharing with your delivery partner you'd like warm tea as you labor. And a mini reminder, you might throw this all away when the time comes but for now we play and let our imaginations experience what they would like.

—ARE *you* LETTING GO?

"Just surrender unto Me. Do not Fear." Bhagavad-Gita 18.66

My intention going into my labor was to surrender. It was to surrender to God, surrender to the wisdom of my body, surrender to the wise women around me--to just surrender. Looking back I struggled with surrender. My mind wanted to control what was happening. My mind didn't want to experience the sensation of pain. My mind didn't want my baby to be in the posterior position. My mind had a different idea of how things would unfold. Here's how things actually went:

December 23, 2018

It's 1:30 am and I can't sleep for so many reasons, including the fact that I am 41 weeks and 4 days pregnant. I say I'm ready for this baby to come, yet the baby hasn't come so we both must not be ready. So I do what I can to distract my mind from the incessant thoughts of *when will it happen already?!* The more I anticipate, the more I push the moment away. I'm reading a book on surrender, the essence being about being very open to the moment we are in. It talks about the energies we might be leaking that keep us from being fully present. I know one of my leaks right now is that I'm holding resentment towards a friend for judging my desire for a natural birth.

I am allowing the moment where she voiced her judgment to follow me around and continue to exist in my present. It's as if I'm carrying her around and she keeps saying, "I'm not sure you can handle a natural birth" in my ear on repeat. She might not feel that way at 1:30 am on December twenty-third, yet I haven't moved past that past moment. So I decide to write her a letter that I will never send, letting her know how I feel. I feel small, I feel like I don't have her support. I feel defensive and I feel angry that I've even allowed her to take up space in my mind.

I finish my venting, I shut off my phone, prop up my many pillows on the couch and say a prayer to sleep. Two hours later I'm awoken by an intense kick from within, followed very quickly by a surge in my body. *Oh, it's happening.* I realize I'm having my first real contraction. I get up and make my way to my bedroom where my husband, Quang, is sleeping soundly. I decide to take a shower before waking him up, I come out fifteen minutes later to another surge. I sit on the edge of the bed, close my eyes and begin my birth mantra. Deep breaths, lots of them. I wake my husband up, "I'm pretty sure it's time," I tell him. He jumps up quickly without even a thought. That's always been one of my favorite things about him. Even if he's in the deepest sleep, if I need him or an ear to listen he's up and wide awake in a snap. He races around the house gathering the things on our list and comes back to time contractions. We message the midwife, she tells us to come in. We might need to go back home but it doesn't hurt for me to get checked. I'm not excited about the idea that we might need to turn around and go all the way back home after all the shifting but I also in my gut knows it is time. The ride over I balanced breathing and thoughts of noticing how quiet the streets were. Gainesville,

Florida becomes a ghost town when the university is not in session. My husband pulls the car as close to the birth center as possible because the Florida girl in me does not like this cold.

Amanda, the midwife I had been working with, is here. She's warm and gentle and checks my cervix. I am six centimeters dilated. She says, "Well, it's go time, you all are staying." Even in the directness of her statement, it doesn't feel real to me. I don't think I want to feel the fullness of this moment. I'm still very scared and wondering if this is actually happening?! Will the baby really join us after all these months? Or maybe it IS possible for my stomach to just stay this way forever, I can just choose to not push!

We pick the room we want, we're the only couple there. I'm reminded of my last appointment with my midwife. When another woman arrived in labor, she labored for just four hours before her baby showed up in her arms. I silently pray that the same is the case for me. A new midwife comes into our room; Amanda is done with being on call and it's Cindy's turn. I feel apprehensive of Cindy being the midwife to deliver my baby. I haven't had much time with her and so I haven't built as much trust. Yet, this is currently what is unfolding; I remind myself of my intention to surrender. She asks how I am, checks the baby's heartbeat. I notice my body begins to tense as contractions continue, Cindy encourages me to do what I need to feel comfortable. I close my eyes and continue my mantra. Contraction after contraction, hour after hour I come back to my mantra -

"Hare Krishna. Hare Krishna. Krishna, Krishna. Hare Hare. Hare Rama. Hare Rama. Rama, Rama. Hare Hare."

Guide me through this God, help me get out of my own way, I plead. Cindy comes in and out. I've progressed to eight centimeters and it's been about six hours. Cindy feels like things are moving a little too slow. I'm secretly okay with just how slow it's going. I say I'm ready to meet this baby but my fear quickly reminds me that I'm not just yet.

We continue to inch forward, the contractions getting stronger and me getting more tired. I lie on the birthing peanut ball. Cindy and my husband take turns squeezing my hips together, the counter pressure feels amazing. The baby is posterior and refuses to turn to be in the optimal position to come out. The feeling of the baby pressing against my tailbone feels like a knife slowly being pressed in. I breathe and I breathe and then I breathe through it some more. I feel triggered each time Cindy shares that I'm not progressing: my internal stories of not being enough keep coming up to the surface. Being in labor feels like my skin has been turned inside out and all my emotions are lying right on top as they pop up. I can feel each moment of anxiety, each moment of relief, each moment of fear. Not one emotion is missed. I consider that maybe I'm not enough to bring this baby into this world - I share with Quang that I need support.

I call a dear friend who is a life coach to support me through my stories that I'm not good enough. She listens as I tell her that I'm triggered and there's just no way I can do this. She encourages me to use my practice, to experience my experience. She encourages Quang to support me in this way too by asking what's happening for me and for me to answer with the words I experience, to fill in the blank with whatever I feel. It helps center me, bring me back to the present moment. The light outside is now dark again, more than sixteen hours later we are still here. And my water hasn't broken. Cindy comes in and suggests we give it a shot to break my water. It might get me into the transition phase of labor. I shudder, I do not want some plastic equipment up where a baby is trying to come out of! I retreat to the bathroom. It feels safe in here. No one to pressure me, just time for me and my baby to connect. I begin to talk to the baby.

I share, "Baby, we are not going to let anyone stick anything inside of us. We are going to break our water bag ourselves, okay?" In that instant I have this deep feeling of connection with the baby, with him. My heart flutters, feeling his heart within my body, that we are together in this journey of birth. I am never alone. Quang and I decided for the whole pregnancy we would wait until the birth to open our present and be surprised. Even with everyone else's guesses I wasn't sure until this bonding of me and him in our little birth center bathroom. I sit as more and more contractions come over me, when to my pleasure and surprise we hear a huge splash. My water just broke. We did it! A huge smile crosses over my face. I knew in my whole heart we could do it.

It's still late, though, and Cindy is worried about me being exhausted post birth. I want to labor more; I'm not ready to give up my natural labor. Yet the surges are getting more and more intense and I'm beginning to believe Cindy might be right. We try getting in the tub, we try music, we try more pressing on my hips. I am now ten centimeters dilated and the baby still hasn't dropped into my pelvis. Cindy makes the tough call that I have been unwilling to make. It's time to make our way to the hospital. Every fear that I've had comes over my body. I'm going to be in the car ten centimeters dilated?! With contractions!? No way. No way. Cindy encourages that it's only a five-minute drive and will be much faster than an ambulance. I haven't slept a wink for now twenty hours. I'm exhausted so I surrender.

My husband remains my rock. He puts a smile on and says, *okay, we can do this.* He packs all our things again and remains calm. I have an intense gratitude wash over me for him. They place me into the back seat of the car where I grab onto the handle of the seat with all of my strength left. With all of my praying, I don't have a contraction in the car. It's mantra time again. The ride is the most intense slowed down version of a five-minute ride I've taken in my life. We pull into the hospital. Cindy is waiting for me at the door.

As soon as I exit the car I'm greeted by an intense contraction. Cindy quickly comes around and presses on my hips and I breathe a big breath. Okay, time to walk to labor and delivery. The team--three nurses, one anesthesiologist--all rush in to help like a scene in *Grey's Anatomy*. They ask me if I want an epidural? Hell yes! Bring on the numbness. They check all my vitals and have me sign a paper as another contraction is coming in so we can make the epidural happen. So much fear arises. A needle is going to go into my back, possibly as I am contracting, and I will need to remain still. I'm scared but I know in my heart I can do it even with the pain sensations. I take three deep breaths, brace myself to feel intensity, yet it barely feels painful. Funny how the mind can anticipate something but when the moment arrives, it's usually absolutely nothing like what the mind expected.

Ah, it's in. Numbness has come to the rescue! The team encourages me to take a nap; in a couple of hours we will try pushing. I encourage my husband to get some rest. We both escape to our little areas of the hospital room for a few hours. I don't sleep one wink, but I do allow myself to rest to hopefully be able to push this baby out. *Please God, let this baby come out* is all I can keep thinking. A few hours go by and the rounding OB comes by to check on me. I haven't dilated further but they do believe I can try pushing. My legs are like jelly, how will I EVER push? Do I even know how to push? Feelings of doubt and failure fill my heart. The nurse whispers in my ear, *let's give this a shot, shall we?* I take a deep breath, I notice the team of loving people around me ready to support me to push. I breathe again and "bear down." I feel nothing. They count me down again, *bear down, Payal. Bear down.* I have zero idea if anything is happening but I'm still using every sliver of energy in me to make this happen. The OB offers a possibility. We can try a tool to help pull the baby out, she gives me and my husband a moment to consider this possibility.

Inside, I want no part of it. I'm beginning to surrender to the idea of a C-section. I'm exhausted and it's been over thirty-six hours (at least) since this labor journey began. I talk it out with my husband and a dear friend. In my heart I knew I didn't want it, but I allowed myself to get influenced so here we were again trying to push with this tool. Push, bear down, Puuuuuuuush, bear down. Nothing. Absolutely nothing. The OB gently apologizes, "I'm sorry, sweetie." At this point, I am surrendered. God, let this be your will not mine.

They wheel me into the operating room, the anesthesiologist treats me with the most gentle care. The whole room feels like a Grey's Anatomy scene. There's music playing, doctors humming along. They've done this a million times, so for them nothing new is happening. My husband arrives by my side with a force of love and care. He's nervous for me yet remains a fortress of love for me. The OB arrives, the cut, cut, cut and then... we hear that glorious sound. "It's a boy!" I don't cry, in all realness I was in a haze. Did I just finally birth a human?

They hand him over to my husband. As he looks at him in awe, Quang brings our son right to my chest. All of this surrender, all of these moments led to this moment. To see my son in all of his glory, his beauty. He has the most luscious lips, eyes with the depth of a well of love, and presence. He had arrived, with his great energy of presence and love. I felt the magic around this moment. The stars had aligned for us. It was written in the stars that two became three and Zayn Kumar Tran entered this world after months of being held in my body - this moment on Christmas Eve was the moment he was meant to enter the world. This was the moment I was meant to be born as a mother. Not a moment sooner, not a moment later.

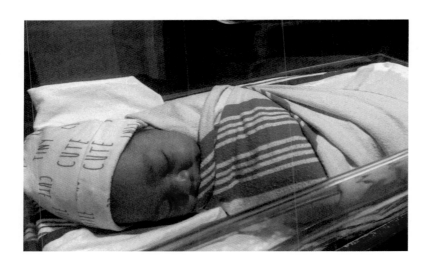

— BEYOND *Pregnancy,* ON LOVING OURSELVES

I am 39 years old and I'm still practicing loving myself. I don't love myself, I practice loving myself.

I became a first-time mom about 3 years ago. I've been mildly successful in life and I love kids - I couldn't screw this up that badly, could I? When I had my son, every unloving thought about myself came up.

> "What am I doing wrong??"
> "Why isn't this easier for me?"
> "Everyone else is great at this...."

One time as I bounced him on this yoga ball to sleep for the 1000th time (a ball I thought would be used only during my pregnancy), I became enraged.

"Why the hell is this happening?"
 "Why am I not a better mother who can get her child to sleep?"
"I am so damn tired!!"

I wasn't angry at my son. I wasn't angry at the bouncing. I was angry at life. I wanted it to be perfect. I wanted my life to look like the storybooks said it would when I finally got that precious baby and it didn't. I was angry that I couldn't figure this motherhood thing out. Just like other times I had failed, here I was also failing at motherhood.

This feeling of hate that silently lived in me for years rose into my mind. It told me that I was not lovable, it said I had failed at being a mother and "winning" life. It told me that everyone else out there had that storybook life and I did not, so I was not worthy of love. Normally I would resist this voice and distract myself with something mindless on TV or a sugary snack. But this time instead of arguing with it and pushing it away, I watched. Instead of stopping this narrative of hate, I listened. I listened to the pain that was disguised as hate that needed to be seen and heard. Maybe it was the years of mindfulness practice that got me to listen, maybe it was the fact that I hadn't slept in days but I was so grateful that this time I allowed myself to listen to what needed to be heard.

It surprised me that I had gone almost 31 years with this pain and hatred living within me, whispering stories into my ears. In my bouncing as I watched and listened and took steady deep breaths, a realization arrived that spoke firmly beyond that voice of hate. It told me that unless I was willing to meet this narrative **with compassion**, I wouldn't be able to meet my son with compassion. It shared that unless I truly was willing to fall in love with myself, I could not love my son.

I couldn't pretend anymore that when I said the words, 'I love you.' I actually had no idea what the **practice** of love meant.

Months later, as I sat with my mentor, I shared that story of hatred of myself with him. He didn't tell me what I needed, he asked me what I thought I needed. Right away I knew what I needed. I told him I needed to talk to my inner little girl.

Now I've been told by mentors, coaches, therapists alike to talk to my inner little girl and I tried--but I wasn't truly talking to her. I would talk over her and at her, intellectually fooling myself that I had done the work.

This time I really wanted to see her and listen to her without all my preconceived notions of her.

I dug up a few old photos of her and showed up at a dear friend's house. We prayed to God, opened our hearts by singing a song to the Lord and I laid out the pictures of little Payal in front of me.

I had written a letter to her and I thought I just wanted to be witnessed reading it. So, I began to read.

'Dear little Payal, I'm so sorry for not really listening to you for so many years. I'm sorry I pushed you away, I'm sorry I blamed you for all that has unfolded in my life.' The tears started rolling down my cheeks, I stopped reading, I looked down at the photos of my little 5-year-old girl smiling back at me. She sat there looking back at me - playful, firm, trusting.

In that moment, I saw something I hadn't seen in 30 plus years - strength. She has so much strength to continue to live life even though she had been violated as a little girl. She has so much resiliency--not in spite of what happened to her but because of what happened to her.

She chooses to still move through life trusting and sharing with others. She has so much strength. In that moment, I understood beyond my own filters of hate. I saw her as she is and transformed that hatred into love.

I finally loved my little girl.

I no longer blamed her for what she had experienced. I no longer blamed her for doing what any 7-year-old would do. I felt compassion for her innocence, I felt compassion for her being her true self and I felt compassion for her perseverance.

Falling in love with me wasn't what I thought it would look like. It wasn't treating myself or showering myself with material love. It was being willing to see my inner little girl without the judgment I placed on her. I judged my little 5 year old self for not speaking up, for not yelling at the rooftops that someone was making her do things that no 5 year old should ever have to do. I judged her for hiding, and pretending that everything was ok when it was not. I judged her for not completely understanding just how wrong it was. My son was my gateway to see this little girl, to understand with empathy the movements of a young child. I noticed how he moved with curiosity and innocence. He was open to receiving without conditions. I saw that he kept trying beyond when I myself would have given up. He showed up with so much presence and a full embodiment of play.

I wonder what falling in love with yourself looks like? Have you checked in with your little girl? Does she need to be heard or given a space of compassion?

Most importantly, this love isn't a one-time thing. It's a continual practice to love me and my little girl. A question I've learned to ask myself when I catch myself shouting negative thoughts to myself, from author Kamal Ravikant, is: 'If I loved myself truly and deeply, would I let myself experience this?'

How would you talk to yourself if you truly and deeply loved yourself? How would you act if you truly and deeply loved yourself?

If we want to love others from a place of compassion, a place of empathy, we must fall in love with ourselves. We must be willing to practice with that listening ear. We must be willing to see with eyes beyond our own judgment. We must be willing to practice compassion to our own selves.

Falling in love with yourself can happen at 10, it can happen at 20, it can happen at 50. Whenever it happens, it's a practice! You might start small, you might start big; whatever it is, never give up practicing falling in love with yourself.

For this exercise you will need a picture of yourself from at least 2 years ago. Sit down and get comfortable. Look at that picture and write down all the first thoughts that come to mind as you look at yourself. As you complete that, do your best to remember the state that you were in as you were in that picture.

What mindset were you in?

. . . .
. . . .
. . . .
. . . .
. . . .
. . . .
. . . .
. . . .
. . . .
. . . .

Where did your thoughts go then?

. . . .
. . . .
. . . .
. . . .
. . . .
. . . .
. . . .

How did you feel emotionally?

What has changed in your view of yourself now and back then?

Have compassion for that past-self knowing what you know now.

Take some time to journal your answers or silently sit in the space of your answers.

— TIPS FOR BEGINNING YOUR MEDITATION PRACTICE

The practice works if we do it.

As mothers and mothers to be we are juggling so much, how will we ever find the time to practice?

It doesn't matter how long or short, it doesn't matter if your meditation space looks like one out of Vogue. It matters that we choose to pay attention. The practice is about noticing when we've checked out of our reality and then consciously bringing ourselves back. For example when we're brushing our teeth and our mind starts to wander into thoughts about things that were left undone from yesterday - we gently bring our attention back to the awareness of the space we are in now - the sound of the running water, the way the bristles feel on our teeth, the taste of our toothpaste. The practice can happen anytime and anywhere.

Find something you already do and add to it.

If you drink water every morning, add 3 deep breaths after you drink. Make it easy for yourself to remember to choose to practice to bring your attention to the present moment. Find a habit you do every single day, it's already in your routine and now you add a 2 minute space to check in with yourself and your breath.

Find the pockets of space to bring awareness to your breath.

In the line at the grocery store? Waiting for something to cook? On hold on the phone with the doctor? Take 3 deep breaths. That's it. Let your breath be the only thing you pay attention to. Sense where you feel your breath most easily, as the rise and fall of your chest, as the expanding and contracting of your belly, or as the way the breath enters your nostrils. Awareness of our breath can be a foundation we build upon as we continue to practice. In each of our days there are pockets we can find to breathe a little space into.

Give yourself grace.

This practice has many starts and stops to it. Some weeks we notice every day, some weeks we barely get one day of practicing in. Grace is essential to remember it's ok to stop and then start again just like the moments we are in.

"When we dance, the journey itself is the point, as when we play music the playing itself is the point. And exactly the same thing is true in meditation. Meditation is the discovery that the point of life is always arrived at in the immediate moment."
- Alan Watts

— CONCLUSION

There is a part of me that would like to leave you with saying that "presence and surrender" are an endpoint, a destination we will reach. Then I remember that in a practice there is no ending. Presence and surrender are a continual practice and sometimes there's even a feeling like we've come back to the very beginning. This practice is a spiral that sometimes moves up and sometimes moves down but we do keep moving in an upward motion. My encouragement is to be a loving witness to the being that is becoming. Practice with the meditations that go along with this book. Reread this book and keep coming back to practice. Practice with a friend, practice with yourself, practice with your baby. Trust in surrendering to the moment and to your highest guidance within *without any borders*.

— ACKNOWL-
EDGMENTS

It is through the grace of the Lord that this book became manifested. Soli Deo Gloria.

I'm eternally grateful to:

Javier Espinosa, your beautiful design work and kindly receiving my multiple edits (the editing never ends!), and encouraging me to finish - it continued to water my seed of desire to make this book happen. Sarah Boon, your illustrations gave my book more life. Janani Krishnaswami and Maria Americano, your editing encouragement gave me energy to dig deeper.

David Wolf, Marie Glasheen, and Leah Sherer - your accountability and support through this process was a gift greater than I can ever repay. Thank you all for reminding me to always remember the 1 in front of the 0's with your way of being in this world.

My husband Quang, you've never given up on me even when I felt like it. Thank you for being by my side on this book journey and the journey of life.

My precious son Zayn, you inspire me every single moment and you inspire me the most to be urgent with my life. Thank you for making me a mother.

My parents and dear brother Gaurav. Thank you all for believing in me with your whole being and continuing to support my love for words and desire to write my first book.

To all of my loving chosen family/friends. So many of you have planted a seed for this book - thank you. Thank you for your unconditional love and support. It's with your presence in my life that life becomes sweet.

The Creative Alchemy Grant Committee. Thank you all for believing in this book being out in the world and supporting its very first print run.

— ABOUT
The AUTHOR

Like many entrepreneurs, Payal considers herself devoted. Her deepest devotion? Supporting others to serve the moment with intention and unwavering presence. She was born in India, raised in Tampa, Fl and went to the University of Florida to get her BS in Computer Engineering. She spent 8 years working in healthcare IT and living all over the country, until she realized that something was missing. With a self-reflective lifestyle and over 9 years of a meditation practice, a growing awareness of her discomfort in the corporate world led her to leave New York City. Back in Gainesville after a long hiatus, she co-founded Starter Space, a co-working space. She later created a 6-week mindfulness program to support others with tools to move through disconnection, distraction and dissatisfaction.

Payal leans into her rich Indian heritage of meditation and travels the world to share the transformative power of presence and deep listening. From individuals to corporations to top rated universities, her work has been a driving force in bringing meditation to modern culture. Payal's thoughtfully crafted, immersive experiences invite self-discovery, inspire transformation and creativity, and provoke meaningful connection. She has been invited to speak about mindfulness for companies such as Ted, eMerge Americas, Trivago, and more.

In 2018, she founded and invited thousands of people into the doors of Gainesville's very first mindfulness studio. Pregnancy and Presence is Payal's first book. She currently spends her time in Alachua, Fl with her husband and son near her Bhakti Yoga spiritual community.

◇◇◇◇◇◇◇◇◇◇◇◇◇◇

@payal_khurana
Visit http://www.payalkhurana.com/

Made in the USA
Monee, IL
10 September 2022

13562968R00069